The Queen likes to dress smartly.

So she has an enormous wardrobe for her clothes . . .

THE
QUEEN'S KNICKERS

NICHOLAS ALLAN

Red Fox

To Jenny

A Red Fox Book

Published by Random House Children's Books
20 Vauxhall Bridge Road, London SW1V 2SA

A division of Random House UK Ltd
London Melbourne Sydney Auckland
Johannesburg and agencies throughout the world

7 9 10 8 6

First published by Hutchinson Children's Books 1993

Red Fox edition 1995

Printed in Hong Kong

RANDOM HOUSE UK Limited Reg. No. 954009

ISBN 0 09 928161 9

. . . and a slightly smaller chest of drawers for all her knickers.

Dilys looks after the Queen's knickers.

She has a special trunk for when the Queen goes away.

One day the trunk went *missing*!

It caused a great crisis . . .

. . . and was only *just* sorted out before it reached the NEWS AT TEN.

The trunk had got mixed up . . .

. . . with a picnic hamper.

ROYAL WEDDINGS

STATE FUNERALS

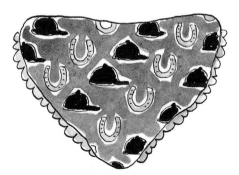

HORSE RIDING
(WITH EXTRA PADDING)

FOREIGN VISITS

The Queen has knick

CKER GUIDE

GARDEN PARTIES

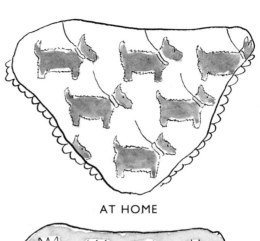

AT HOME

BALMORAL (WOOLLEN)

EVERY DAY

all occasions.

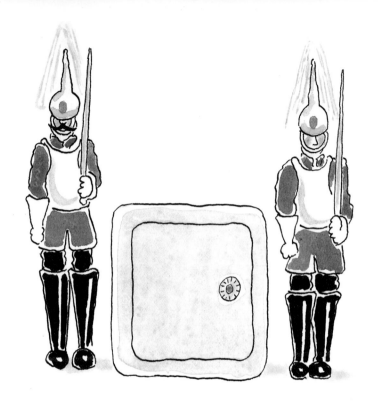

At the opening of Parliament
the Queen wears her VIP's (Very Important Pair).
There is no picture of these. But here is the safe
where they're locked up with other
state secrets.

Pull
cord

When she travels
she has special knickers with a small
parachute inside them . . .

. . . just in case.

(She has another

when she's on board ship.)

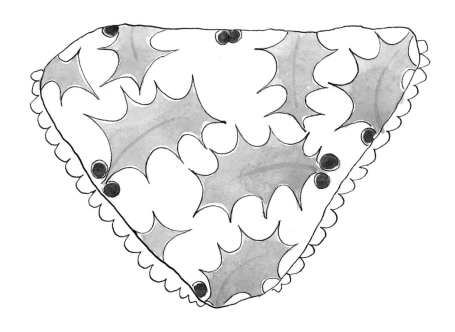

But her most special
knickers are her Christmas knickers.
They are a gift from Scandinavia and are traditionally
decorated with real holly . . .

. . . which is why
she keeps her Christmas
message very short.

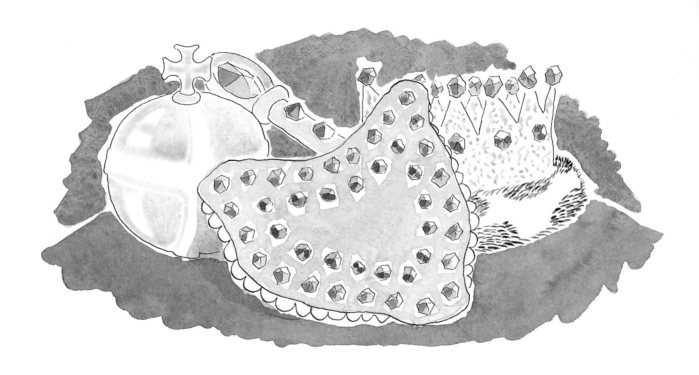

The Royal Knickers, though, are her
most valuable. They are made of pure silk
with gold thread and encrusted with diamonds,
emeralds, and rubies.

They were first worn
by Queen Victoria and are
rather baggy.

I wonder what knickers the Queen would wear
if she visited our school?

There'd be a *terrific* flap at the Palace.

'Call the Royal Knicker-maker, Dilys!'

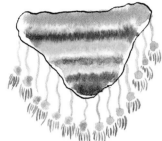

'Oh no! Far too fancy!'

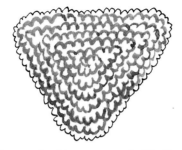

'Oh no! Far too frilly!'

'Oh no! Far too plain!'

'Oh no! Far too . . . SILLY!'

'I shall just have to wear my "Every Day" knickers.'

Then the poor Queen would feel very awkward,
as she's so particular about her clothes.

But I would tell her something to put her at ease.
'Don't worry about your knickers, Your Majesty,' I'd whisper.
'You see, *no one can see them anyway.*'

Then she'd be sure to send a special note
to me afterwards by the Royal Mail saying:

*'Her majesty wishes
to inform you that her
visit was most enjoyable...
and very comfortable.'*